Bougainville copper mine, Papua New Guinea — the fourth largest copper mine in the world.

COPPER
AND COPPER MINING

R. L. Atkinson

Shire Publications Ltd

CONTENTS

Copper and its uses 3
History 10
Copper mining in Britain 15
Mining, processing and smelting 23
Further reading 31
Mining societies 31
Places to visit 32

Set in 9 point Times roman and printed in Great Britain by C. I. Thomas & Sons (Haverfordwest) Ltd, Press Buildings, Merlins Bridge, Haverfordwest, Dyfed.

British Library Cataloguing in Publication Data available.

ACKNOWLEDGEMENTS

I am indebted to my friends and colleagues at the Camborne School of Mines for their help in the preparation of this book. Thanks are also due to Mr R. Penhallurick of the Royal Institution of Cornwall for his assistance. Photographs are acknowledged to: Dr K. Atkinson, page 3, 32; Dr D. E. B. Bates, page 19; Dr A. V. Bromley, pages 6, 7, 8 (upper), 18 (upper), 20 (lower), 30; Camborne School of Mines, 4 (upper), 5, 11, 16 (lower); Mr E. G. Holland, page 22; Mr N. Hoyland, page 21; IMI Refiners Ltd, cover; Mr W. Longley-Cook, page 12 (lower); Morwellham Recreation Company Limited, page 15; Mount Isa Mine, page 8 (lower); Royal Institution of Cornwall, pages 2, 4 (lower), 9, 16 (upper), 17, 18 (lower), 23, 24, 25, 26, 27; RTZ Services Limited, page 1; South Australian Bureau of Mines and Energy, pages 10, 12 (upper), 13, 14, 28, 29; Welsh Industrial and Maritime Museum, page 20 (upper).

COVER: *Copper pouring at IMI Refiners Limited, James Bridge Copper Works, Walsall.*

BELOW: *Late bronze age copper 'bun ingots' found at Gillan Creek, Cornwall, in the 1930s, and now in the Cornwall County Museum. The hollow copper axe found nearby is dated to between 900 and 500 BC. It measures 60 by 30 mm (2¼ by 1¼ inches).*

Bingham Canyon open pit, Utah, USA, the first mine to exploit low-grade porphyry copper ore. It grew from a small underground mine working 6 per cent vein ore to a massive open pit with huge reserves of 0.75-2.5 per cent copper. Trains on the lower benches give an idea of scale.

COPPER AND ITS USES

Most metals must be extracted from their ores but a few are found in a more or less pure state. Gold and silver occur in this way, but natural copper metal is far more common and has been found on every continent. Early man discovered that copper could be fashioned into tools or beaten into sheets and moulded into vessels stronger and more durable than simple clay pots. Polished copper made quite a good mirror. The sheer beauty of burnished metal gave it supernatural importance. It was revered, like fire, as a gift from the sun.

It was the development of smelting, however, which marked the transition to the age of metals. The technique was probably discovered by potters using copper minerals to produce coloured glazes. Primitive bellows provided the high temperatures needed and metal could have been produced accidentally. It was soon found that copper could be mixed with tin and zinc to make bronze and brass alloys which were superior in strength and durability.

Copper is the eighth most abundant metal in the earth's crust and is found in over 160 different minerals. Before the twentieth century high-grade deposits, from small underground mines, were the main source of copper. Until 2000 BC the grade was as high as 15 per cent, by AD 1500 it had dropped to 9 per cent and by 1800 to about 6 per cent. From 1904 this changed dramatically with the discovery of large deposits averaging only 0.5 per cent which could be worked cheaply. The first mine to exploit these ores was at Bingham, Utah, USA, which grew from an underground mine working 6 per cent ore to a massive open pit working 0.75 to 2.5 per cent copper.

The small mines have now disappeared and large, low-grade 'porphyry' copper deposits are exploited. The most important mineral is chalcopyrite (copper iron sulphide), scattered through immense volumes of rock. Reserves are as big as hundreds of millions of tonnes and ore is mined in very large open pits. Most porphyry deposits are associated with

3

Dendritic native copper, Wheal Unity, Cornwall, 120 mm (4¾ inches) long, in Camborne School of Mines Geological Museum.

young rocks (75 million years old or less), mainly around the Pacific Ocean. The Ok-Tedi deposit in Papua New Guinea is only about 1.2 million years old. Similar deposits may be still forming in the roots of active volcanoes. Gold, silver and molybdenum are important by-products, often keeping mines viable in times of depressed copper prices.

Stratiform, or bedded, copper deposits

The Youlton bronze bowl found at Higher Youlton Farm, Cornwall, during the draining of a peat bog in 1925. It was finished on a lathe and probably dates to the first century AD. Its diameter is 190 mm (7½ inches) and it is now in the Cornwall County Museum, Truro.

4

ABOVE: *Copper minerals: (top) malachite from Zaire, banded, green, 170 by 120 mm (6¾ by 4¾ inches); (centre row, from left) bournonite in quartz, Cornwall, grey, 80 by 60 mm (3¼ by 2¼ inches); chalcopyrite, Cornwall, golden, 110 by 70 mm (4¼ by 2¾ inches); azurite, France, blue, 120 by 100 mm (4¾ by 4 inches); (bottom row, from left) tetrahedrite, Cornwall, grey, 80 by 70 mm (3¼ by 2¾ inches); cuprite, Cornwall, dark red, 80 by 50 mm (3¼ by 2 inches); native copper, Siberia, 70 by 70 mm (2¾ by 2¾ inches).*

BELOW: *Chalcopyrite, copper iron sulphide, showing various habits: (top left) botryoidal; (top right) massive; (bottom left) crystalline, with quartz; (bottom right) disseminated.*

Major Copper Mining Regions

World copper deposits — location map.

KEY

1. Butte
2. Bingham
3. Bisbee
4. Michigan
5. Sudbury
6. Cerro de Pasco
7. Chuquicamata
8. Avoca
9. Harz Mountains
10. Rio Tinto
11. Cyprus
12. Timna
13. The Copper Belt
14. Tsumeb
15. O'okiep
16. Ok Tedi
17. Bougainville
18. Mount Isa
19. Olympic Dam
20. Burra
21. Walleroo
22. Kapunda
23. Moonta
24. Mount Lyell

are found in some sedimentary and volcanic rocks. The *Kupferschiefer* of central Europe (less than 1 metre, 3 feet, thick) was originally an organic mud in which copper, lead and zinc accumulated. Geologists think that hot, metal-rich brines streamed out through fissures in the seabed and as they mixed with sea water metal sulphides were deposited amongst the accumulating sediment. Similar ores occur in Bolivia, Morocco, Zambia, Zaire, the USA and the USSR.

America has many important copper deposits. Canadian mines and those in the south-western USA date from the 1880s. In South America the great excavation of Chuquicamata lies deep within the Atacama desert of northern Chile and in the Andes copper is worked at Cerro de Pasco in Peru, 5000 metres (16,000 feet) above sea level. In central Africa the famous Copper Belt extends through Zimbabwe, Zambia and Zaire. Mines in this area produce many thousands of tonnes of copper every year. In Namaqualand in western South Africa copper has been known since the time of Vasco da Gama (about 1500) but has only been exploited since the 1850s. Asia and Australasia had huge copper mines and many new deposits were discovered in the 1980s — Ok-Tedi came into production in 1984. Australia has copper mines as far apart as Queensland and Tasmania.

In Europe Norwegian and Swedish mines were worked for centuries and the Harz Mountains in Germany were famous for their mines and skilful miners. At various times copper ore was mined and smelted in England, Scotland, Ireland and Wales.

Uses of copper changed over the centuries. By the 1650s nearly half the copper produced in Britain was made into wire. In Surrey a wireworks had water-powered machinery and the finished product was cleaned with rotten oranges. Birmingham and Bristol became famous for their brass foundries where cylinders, valves and taps were made. Dies and moulds could be fabricated easily and mass production began with the manufacture of coins at thirty thousand an hour. This was the beginning of the industrial revolution. At Sheffield silver-plating on to copper was developed for cutlery and tableware. A hundred years later the greatest demand was for copper to protect the hulls of ships from wood-boring creatures.

The special properties of copper make it as useful today as ever. Its high electrical and thermal conductivity is exploited in many instruments. Stranded copper wire carries electricity and telephone messages. The ease with which it can be soldered makes it suitable for many purposes: bolts, nails, rivets, jewellery, springs, clocks and so on. Copper

RIGHT: *Graph showing grades of copper worked. Before the twentieth century high-grade deposits, worked in small underground mines, were the main source of copper. Until 2000 BC the grade was perhaps as high as 15 per cent; by AD 1500 it had dropped to 9 per cent; from 1904 this changed dramatically with the discovery that large deposits with an average of only 0.5 per cent copper could be worked economically.*

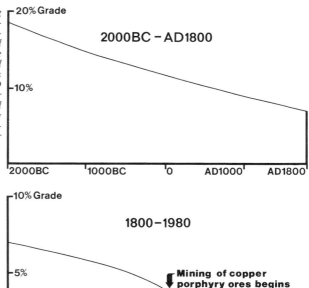

20% Grade

2000BC – AD1800

10%

2000BC   1000BC   0   AD1000   AD1800

10% Grade

1800–1980

5%

↓ **Mining of copper porphyry ores begins**

1800   1850   1900   1940   1980

BELOW: *Mount Isa mine and town, Queensland, Australia. The copper-lead-zinc ore is very important. The shorter, striped stack is the copper smelter, the tall stack is the lead and zinc smelter.*

Mining in the Harz Mountains, Germany, at the end of the nineteenth century. Although this view is similar to the Cornish mining scenes the clothing is characteristically German. Arch supports and heavy timbering was needed in these mines.

has good mechanical properties of high tensile strength, ductility and resistance to corrosion. It is readily electro-deposited and used for plating other metals. Even in modern times its attractive appearance is used by architects, artists and decorators, although its major uses are in batteries, generators, motors, transformers and telecommunications. Small amounts of copper are essential for the proper growth of plants and animals and new uses have been found for copper salts. Non-toxic copper-based products are used in fertilisers, insecticides and fungicides.

Because copper is virtually indestructible, scrap is an important commodity. Scrapyards are sometimes referred to as 'mines above the ground'. Copper can be recycled at the melting and refining stage as new scrap (shavings or swarf) or old scrap (from machines, old telephone equipment and old buildings). Brassmakers use scrap as a raw material or it is re-refined. About 40 per cent of available copper is recycled. Though there is competition from aluminium, plastics and stainless steel, copper is so versatile that it will find a place in our economy for many decades to come.

Walleroo mines, South Australia, early twentieth century. Drilling blast holes with jackhammers. Stopes were worked by contract miners in teams of four with another four to help with transport. Some stopes were only 1 metre (3 feet 3 inches) wide.

HISTORY

Copper was important in the great civilisations of the past. In the Sinai desert of Egypt sandstone cliffs have deposits of cuprite, chalcocite, malachite and azurite. Here lies Timna, the 'cradle of industry', where smelting dates from 4000 BC. Four thousand years ago copper was won from underground mines in the eastern Mediterranean. The word copper comes from the Latin *cyprium*, meaning 'ore of Cyprus'. The Romans worked copper oxides but could not recover metal from sulphides, which became more abundant as the workings deepened. Noticing that water dripping through the mines contained copper sulphate, they drove tunnels underneath to catch the solution, which they could use. Tunnels often collapsed crushing the slave miners and the deposits were abandoned and forgotten for almost two thousand years.

In Spain the red-coloured water of the Rio Tinto flows from the foothills of the Sierra Morena. In the thirteenth century BC Phoenician traders followed the red river inland and found copper. At the surface were soft, decomposed rocks with rich oxides below. These were easily quarried; charcoal was used for smelting. By 1100 BC this was a major centre of copper production. When Carthage annexed Spain armies of slaves worked the mines. Copper became important again under the Romans and was exported all over the known world. Towns grew up, supplied by roads and aqueducts which can still be seen. When the Roman empire ceased expanding and slaves were not so easily procured, better working conditions were needed and labour laws evolved which rival those of some modern mines. The financial crisis caused when the mines were abandoned may have contributed to the destruction of the empire.

Mining techniques used by the Romans are well known. Quicklime was rammed into fissures and soaked with water to make it expand, forcing the rock apart.

Alternatively fires were lit against the rocks, which were then drenched with water to make them shatter. Oil lamps were the only light in the mines and men carried ore to the surface in leather buckets, climbing up notched poles. Later hand windlasses were developed for haulage in vertical shafts. Flooding was overcome initially by slaves with buckets, then by waterwheels, turned by slaves, raising water from one level to another. Though the Romans used only small smelters the slag left shows hardly a trace of copper.

During the middle ages the Moorish invaders of Spain worked in iron and steel, reserving copper for pots and ornaments. At Rio Tinto the copper oxides were exhausted but water draining through the old workings slowly attacked the sulphides, carrying the metal away as copper sulphate. By allowing the solution to flow over scrap copper was precipitated. Iron was cheap and abundant and the area prospered. In the seventeenth and eighteenth centuries other Europeans were prospecting for copper and in 1873 a British company spent nearly £4 million on buying land in the region. A new discovery helped the company to prosper: if the ore heaps were set on fire and then leached with water, copper was produced faster. Again Rio Tinto became a great copper producer.

When America was discovered the Indians were still living in the stone age. They wore ornaments of pure copper but had never learnt to harden it. Early settlers were too busy to look for the source of this copper and not until several centuries later were ancient copper mines discovered in Michigan and then copper boulders in glacial drift were traced northwards to the shore of Lake Superior. Rediscovered, the area reached its peak of production by the end of the nineteenth century; since then there has been a steady decline and the ore is no longer economic.

In the nineteenth century there were gold and silver rushes in North America but when these were exhausted prospectors turned to copper. In Butte, Montana, in 1877 high-grade copper ore over 15 metres (50 feet) wide was discovered and the Anaconda became the richest copper mine in the world. Stamp mills crushed the ore night and day. Lawsuits and gang warfare between rival mine

Wooden logs, partly replaced by copper metal; 120 mm (4¾ inches) diameter. Specimens like these are found in the old Roman workings in Cyprus. The island was an important source of the metal for the Greek and Roman world.

ABOVE: *Copper leaching at Pernatty Lagoon, South Australia, 1915. This method of copper extraction was discovered at Rio Tinto, Spain. In the 'outback' camels were used for general haulage.*

LEFT: *Modern workings at Rio Tinto, Spain. The 100 tonne trucks in the pit give an idea of the size of the operation. Often old underground workings of previous centuries are found in the excavations.*

Walleroo smelters, South Australia, 1910-20. As with most smelters the fumes could be seen for a great distance and became a well known landmark.

owners were commonplace. At Bisbee, Arizona, deposits of copper carbonate were found. In the narrow gulch living conditions were abysmal. There was room for only one street and insanitary ghettos grew up on the hillsides above. Many Cornishmen and Mexican miners came but flash floods and landslides frequently devastated the township. Eventually the smelters were moved,

A twenty-head stamp battery in South Australia, 1880s. This is typical of stamps in use at most copper mines of the period.

more streets and better housing appeared and a hospital and library were built.

The economic development of Australia was dominated by the discovery of copper. By 1860 South Australia was called the 'Copper Kingdom'. The first major find was at Kapunda in 1842. The ore was so rich that it was shovelled directly into carts for transport to Port Adelaide and shipment to the smelters of South Wales. Cornish miners were brought in when underground mining began. A horse whim, then steam engines were erected and in 1849 a smelter was built. When copper was discovered at Burra in 1845 much wood was needed for pit props — fifty thousand logs at first, then ten thousand every few months. The smelters also used 600 tonnes of wood each week and the landscape was soon laid bare. A thousand men and four thousand bullocks worked at the mine. Though Burra became open-cast in 1867 drainage remained a severe problem. Water was pumped out and carried to a waterwheel which drove a stamp battery. In the 1860s Moonta and Kadina became the world's largest copper producers. They were labour intensive and not mechanised until after 1900. Moonta was called 'Australia's Little Cornwall', with a population of ten thousand mostly of Cornish extraction. Goats were a local pest and goat meat became an ingredient of Cornish pasties along with rabbit, kangaroo and wallaby. A hundred years later new exploration led to the re-opening of several mines. In 1975 Olympic Dam, one of the largest copper-gold-uranium deposits in the world, was discovered.

The great old copper mines had met the world's needs for ten thousand years but the age of electricity increased demand by many times. A luxury in the 1850s, copper became a necessity. When the old mines were exhausted at the end of the nineteenth century it was thought that the metal would become scarce but new and different ore bodies were found.

The pumping engine at Moonta mines, South Australia, which worked from 1865 to 1923. The vertical rod was 800 metres (2600 feet) long and was powered by a steam engine with three boilers. The influence of Cornish engineers is well illustrated here.

Morwellham Quay, Devon, about 1868, the busiest inland port west of Exeter. Copper ore can be seen stacked on the quays. One of the inclines is to the Tavistock canal, the other to the Devon Great Consols minerals railway. In the mid nineteenth century the Tamar valley was Europe's chief source of copper.

COPPER MINING IN BRITAIN

Copper mining was an important activity in the British Isles in places as distant as the Shetlands and Land's End. The first mine would be impossible to date, a small working leaving no trace; the last major copper mine at Avoca in the Irish Republic closed down in 1982. Of all the areas in Britain where copper was mined none was more important than south west England.

CORNWALL

There has been mining in Cornwall since very early times and from archaeological evidence mining and smelting can be traced to prehistoric times. Tin is usually thought the most important metal in the area but between 1700 and 1850 copper was of equal or greater importance. Many innovations in the industry came from the mining engineers of Cornwall. The steam engine invented by Thomas Newcomen was introduced at Wheal Vor, near Helston, in 1715. By 1778 sixty engines were at work in the west of England. James Watt greatly improved the efficiency of steam and in 1811 Richard Trevithick from Camborne produced a high-pressure steam engine. It was a Cornishman, William Bickford of Camborne, who invented the safety fuse in 1831. Cornish miners travelled around Britain taking their skills and customs to other mining areas. In 1836 the great Dolcoath copper mine turned over to producing tin. But in 1985 750 tonnes of copper metal were still produced from the tin mines of Cornwall.

DEVON

The five largest mines which dominated the industry were Devon Great Consols, Bedford United, Wheal Maria, Wheal Friendship and Wheal Crebor. Fortunately the Tamar mines lay in a deep valley so they could be drained by adits; Wheal Friendship was worked by thirteen massive waterwheels and two leats 3 km (2 miles) and 8 km (5 miles) long.

15

ABOVE: *Horse whim at Levant, Pendeen, Cornwall. With the introduction of the powerful beam engine, waterwheels and horse whims became redundant. Photograph by H. W. Hughes, 1903.*

LEFT: *East Pool engine house near Camborne is still operational and opened to visitors by the National Trust. The basic design of the Cornish beam engine came from Thomas Newcomen and was used at Wheal Vor in 1715. By 1778 sixty engines were at work in south-west England.*

ABOVE: *Engine-house interior. New ideas from James Watt, Richard Trevithick and Arthur Woolf further improved the high-pressure steam engine.*

BELOW: *Dolcoath copper mine, Camborne, Cornwall, engraved by J. Thomas after a drawing by Thomas Allom; from 'Cornwall Illustrated' by J. Britton and E. W. Brayley, 1831. Notice the bal maidens at work in the foreground.*

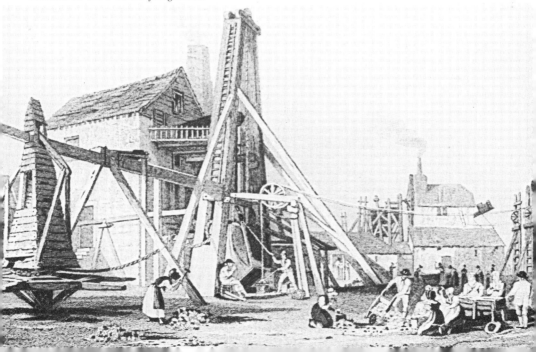

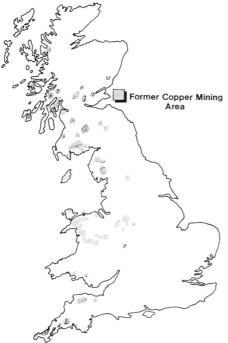

Former Copper Mining Area

During the first half of the nineteenth century Devon increased its output of copper dramatically, but by 1870 the price had fallen and British output halved. Even the rich Tamar valley mines cut back production, although they weathered the recession better than those of Cornwall. By 1886 Devon produced half of Britain's copper. In the last decade of the nineteenth century Devon Great Consols produced 98 per cent of British copper. In 1901 the mine was forced to close, machinery was sold and the site levelled: six thousand inhabitants of Tavistock had depended on the mine for 55 years.

WALES

The earliest mines in Wales were opencast copper and lead workings. In the north at Llandudno, Gwynedd, a small Roman mine is thought to have been worked by slaves and convicts. Ore seems to have been smelted locally and a large copper slab found near Conway, Gwynedd, is probably Roman. Many centuries passed and production was poor but in 1717 smelters in Lancashire recorded receiving Welsh copper. There were many small copper mines in north

ABOVE: *Copper deposits in Britain.*
BELOW: *Gunnislake Clitters mine, Cornwall. The mine began in about 1820 and was worked chiefly for tin within the granite. It was amalgamated with Hingston Down and Old Gunnislake mines in about 1900.*

18

Esgair Hir, near Aberystwyth, Dyfed, 1986, showing the slot for the balance bob of Shaft Glas. On the skyline are the ruins of the steam engine and dumps.

and central Wales, where a few great absentee landlords leased mineral rights on a royalty basis. Before the nineteenth century there was little machinery; hand sorting was carried out in the open air or in crude shelters. The climate was harsh and cold and the mines were so remote that men had to live in barracks on site. In the mountainous countryside roads were very poor. Horizontal adit mining, tunnelling into the valley sides, was comparatively easy: pumping and winding gear was often unnecessary and there are few traces of engine houses. It was difficult to separate lead from copper and the concentrate frequently averaged less than 10 per cent copper. The mines were often run at a loss in the hope of better days.

A few Welsh mines found fame and fortune. The Turf Copper Works near Llanfachreth, Gwynedd, was an unusual deposit with leaves, nuts and wood preserved as copper. The turf was so impregnated with metal that blocks could be sent straight to the smelter. Nearby, at Glasdir, two deep pits produced 10,000 tonnes of ore between 1872 and 1914.

The Mona and Parys mines on Anglesey date at least from Roman times. Local miners paid copper ore as tribute and a fort was built at Caernarfon to protect them. They were begun as shafts and levels but a major collapse was caused by the robbing of roof pillars. After this open pits were developed. Between Roman times and the mid eighteenth century the mines fell into disuse. Then the 'Great Lode' was struck in 1768 — the most productive in Europe. It was not particularly rich but just 2 metres (6 feet) below surface and only 2 km (1¼ miles) from a deep-water port. Mining was controlled by one man, Thomas Williams, thus helping to preserve the unity of the mines, unlike in Cornwall, where there was often bitter rivalry. Williams set up his own smelters to beat the Swansea smelting ring. This brought down the price of copper ore and the Cornish mines suffered badly. In modern times the only production in Anglesey has been from copper sulphate solutions draining from the mines, although some further exploration has taken place in the 1980s.

19

ABOVE: *Parys Copper Mine, Anglesey. A painting by J. C. Ibbetson, about 1800.*
BELOW: *Parys Mountain, Anglesey 1986. After making a profit of over £2.5 million and exploiting 3 million cubic metres (106 million cubic feet) of ore, the pits were finally exhausted in 1880. Early in the twentieth century copper was leached from the dumps and there has been further exploration in the 1970s and 1980s.*

West mine, Alderley Edge, Cheshire, 1985. In 1857 West and Wood mines came into operation. The lower beds of West mine were excavated leaving a great hollow centre with only one quarter of the ground left as pillars.

CHESHIRE

The Alderley Edge mines, south of Manchester, date from the bronze age. Malachite, azurite and chrysocolla are sometimes found in thin veins but copper sulphides are rare. The mineralised gossan (the weathered surface deposit) was worked in small pits but these were mostly obscured by later mining. There are Roman remains but by the time of the Domesday survey (1086) mining had ceased. In the late seventeenth century underground mining flourished. By 1758 the Macclesfield Copper Company operated a smelter taking ore from Cumbria and Staffordshire to make brass. Women worked on the surface 'cobbing' ore for the smelter. At Mottram St Andrew, a quarry 3 km (2 miles) to the east, grades of up to 22 per cent were mined.

Before 1850 some ore was considered uneconomic. Then a new method of extracting copper was discovered. At Alderley Edge crushed copper ore was fed into tanks with enough acid to dissolve about three-quarters of the copper. The liquid dripped through the false bottoms of the tanks, made of brushwood and straw. Every two hours the acid was recycled. Bright green liquid ran off into wooden tanks, where scrap iron and tinplate were added. Flecks of metallic copper were precipitated, taken out and dried.

SHROPSHIRE

There are isolated copper mines in the north-west of the county. Evidence of Roman occupation exists in the galleries of Llanymynech mine south-west of Oswestry and seventeenth-century artefacts have been found. Eardiston mine near Oswestry recorded an average grade of 11.5 per cent copper. No modern copper mining has taken place in the area.

STAFFORDSHIRE

Copper deposits at Ecton Hill, in the north of the county, occur in sharply folded limestones. Mining was difficult. In 1638 Prince Rupert, nephew of Charles I, introduced gunpowder and employed German miners to overcome the problems. Nearly two hundred years later the mines were reworked by Cornishmen. Three great chambers were excavated to recover grades of 15 per cent. Between 1776 and 1817, when the mines closed, over 50,000 tonnes of ore were removed.

THE LAKE DISTRICT

Mineral veins were exploited by ancient British and Roman miners but it was not until Elizabethan times that the industry prospered. The German miner Daniel Houghstetter was brought to Keswick, where rich copper veins had been discovered. German workmen built furnaces, a refinery and a rolling mill. During the Civil War Cromwell's forces destroyed the smelter but forty years later William of Orange used Dutch engineers to re-open the mines. Coniston mines, over 400 metres (1300 feet) deep, produced about three-quarters of all Lake District copper, more than half of it from one vein of chalcopyrite. Other mines in the area included Paddy End mine, which worked into the early years of the twentieth century.

SCOTLAND

Stone moulds have been found, at least four thousand years old, which were used for casting bronze. Native copper was smelted in Bute and at the end of the sixteenth century French miners were brought in to increase production. In the eighteenth century Sandlode mine, in the Shetlands, employed Welsh miners. Native copper was found on the Orkney Isles and at Loch Tay. Rich copper is reported from Bell's Isle though little is known of the mining operations. All over Scotland trial pits and small mines are to be found — perhaps in Kirkcudbrightshire more than in any other area. Enrick mine was the largest and sent ore to Swansea for smelting in the nineteenth century. None of the deposits was very large and copper mining was never of more than local importance in Scotland.

Coniston copper mines in the Lake District, Cumbria, showing the dressing floors of Low Mill, Bonser, in the nineteenth century. Drawing by Eric Holland.

A group of Cornish miners ready to go underground. Candles were stuck to their hardened felt hats while spares were tied together and hung around their necks. In the early days tools were expensive and were often carried tied to the waist to avoid loss in the blackness of the mine.

MINING, PROCESSING AND SMELTING

As native copper became less easy to find bronze age man had to devise ways of extracting the metal from its ores. The earliest mines were no more than 'scratchings' where brightly coloured secondary copper ores outcropped at the surface.

Cornwall was probably one of the first areas in Europe where underground copper mining was carried out. In the Land's End peninsula and around St Agnes lodes are exposed in the steep cliffs and would have been easily discovered. Tin, which could be alloyed with copper to make bronze, was also mined in the region at an early date.

The steeply dipping lodes vary in width between a few centimetres and more than 7 metres (23 feet), and in length between a few metres and hundreds of metres. Bright green and blue secondary ores at the surface give way at greater depth first to rich ores like the grey chalcocite

(redruthite) and iridescent bornite (peacock ore), and then to golden yellow chalcopyrite. Ores of tin, arsenic and other metals often occur along with the copper minerals.

The earliest mines were small open pits or 'coffins', usually only a few metres deep. Underground mining was restricted by drainage; an adit was driven at the lowest possible point to lead water from the workings. In the hilly country of east Cornwall and Devon large mines could have been drained by adits in the deep valleys but in west Cornwall sea-level adits must have limited the scale of underground development.

Much less is known of the early development of copper mining in Cornwall than of tin mining. In Elizabethan times copper was won on a small scale. The ores were broken out by fire setting, quicklime slaking and plug-and-feathering. The last method a stone-quarrying technique, consisted of driving pairs of semicircular wedges into cracks in the rock and forcing them apart by hammering a cone-shaped iron or bronze rod between them. Mines were developed below adit level and dewatered by primitive pumps. The 'rag and chain' pump, described in Agricola's famous book of 1556, *De Re Metallica,* and in Carew's *Survey of Cornwall* (1602), consisted of an endless chain, broadened at intervals by leather bindings, which fitted tightly inside a wooden pipe some 3 to 6 metres (10 to 20 feet) in length. Worked by a handle on a flywheel at the surface and catching up short columns of water between the bindings, it served very well to drain shallow workings. In deeper mines a series of pumps was needed. A 10 cm (4 inch) pump drawing 6 metres (20 feet) needed more than twenty men working in teams of five or six for spells which might be as long as six hours.

A shift, or 'core', in an Elizabethan copper mine lasted only four hours, no doubt because the miners were soon exhausted by continuous heavy manual work in cramped, dark, hot and airless conditions. By the eighteenth and early nineteenth centuries — the heyday of Cornish copper mining — a core might last eight, ten or even twelve hours. Technological progress enabled mines to go deeper, ore to be broken more easily and hoisted to the surface more quickly; the lot of the miner improved only slowly.

Horse whims, waterwheels and eventually the great steam engines of Newcomen, Trevithick and Watt replaced the rag and chain pump. They were used not only for draining the mines but also for hoisting ore. Drainage adits were driven on an unprecedented scale. The famous County Adit, started near Bissoe Bridge in Gwennap, eventually reached a length of 50 km (31 miles) and drained 46 mines, the furthest nearly 9 km (5½ miles) from its mouth. These great adits served an additional purpose in that while they were being driven many new lodes were discovered.

East Pool mine, near Camborne, photographed by J. C. Burrows in the 1880s, showing stoping at the 70 fathom (130 metre) level. Notice the Cornish shovel used as a candlestick and candles on the miners' hats and on rock ledges. At the beginning of the twentieth century acetylene lamps were introduced, then battery-powered cap lamps.

LEFT: *South Condurrow mine, near Camborne, photographed by J. C. Burrows in the 1880s. A miner is clearing an ore chute from the stope above. Horizontal timbers hold back the lumps of ore until the tram is ready for loading. In the eighteenth and nineteenth centuries ore was hand-picked in the stopes before being 'sent to grass' and the waste was left behind. The surrounding rock stood up well and only rarely was heavy propping needed. The ore was blasted at the end of a shift, allowing time for the air to clear.*

RIGHT: *Gigs or cages with wire ropes eventually replaced wooden ladders, which were so arduous and time-consuming to climb after a shift. There were not many of the infamous 'man engines' as shafts were often too narrow and crooked in south-west England.*

Gunpowder, for blasting the rock, was introduced into England by German miners at Ecton copper mines, Staffordshire, in 1670. In Cornwall, it was used in the St Agnes district in 1689 but in the mines of the far west, beyond St Ives, it was not in general use until after 1700. Gunpowder was appallingly dangerous. Accidents from premature explosion and picking out holes which had misfired more often maimed than killed outright. The gradual introduction of Bickford's safety fuse, after 1830, made blasting much less hazardous, but the smoke and fumes, which lingered for hours after firing in badly ventilated ends, were sometimes so thick that candles would burn only if laid on their sides. When nitroglycerine was discovered by Nobel, accidents became less common. Shot holes were bored with 'jumping bars' — long, heavy rods — which were lifted and dropped. The drill rod, called a 'borer' or 'steel', was quicker and could be used by two men hammering alternately.

Almost to the end of the copper mining era in Cornwall men and boys reached their workplaces by climbing wooden ladders. After a walk of several kilometres from home to mine they might have to descend as far as 600 metres (2000 feet), taking three-quarters of an hour to reach the deepest levels. Bad ventilation, oxidising copper ores which gave off heat and natural hot springs made working conditions almost unbearable. In Consolidated Mines, St Day, the temperature reached 42 C (108 F) in the

25

South Australia, early twentieth century. The highest-grade ore was hand-picked from the conveyor belt to send to the smelter. A large number of boys helped with this work in the early days.

ends; hot springs in nearby Wheal Clifford issued from the rock at 52 C (126 F). At Consolidated miners bathed in water at the shaft bottom to cool off; its temperature was 34 C (93 F). After an eight-hour core it was time for the arduous climb back to the surface. A fit young man might take an hour and a quarter, carrying tools and borers weighing nearly 9 kg (20 pounds). Even then the miners' sufferings were not over. There were no proper change houses or drying facilities. In winter they might have to change into clothes frozen solid for the long walk home.

Ore dressing was difficult as chalcopyrite is friable. If the ore was crushed too much, copper was lost in tailings (waste), so hand picking was used. Stamps crushed the ore and young boys, old men and women (the bal maidens) 'cobbed' or hammered the rock and sieved the residue for chalcopyrite.

At each mine a mine captain was appointed by the directors. There were almost two thousand mines altogether; between 1820 and 1870, four hundred active copper mines employed over eighteen thousand men and ten thousand women and children. Mining was financed by 'adventurers' who gambled their capital to gain a fortune. Accounts were kept in a 'cost book' and when these were examined feasts were held, probably to impress the shareholders. This system was ended in the late nineteenth century and ore was sold at 'ticketings', where agents from the smelters sampled ore and made written bids. The South Wales smelters were closely linked and compared bids to keep prices down.

In the earliest smelters copper ore was laid on sticks above a shallow pit. When it was fired molten metal ran into the pit, cooled and was beaten into shape. Later, charcoal was used as fuel and the pit was banked over with clay like a kiln. After firing and removal of the slag a 'bun ingot' remained. Wind was important, for a strong draught was essential to achieve high temperatures, and the 'blowing houses' were often sited on hills. Bellows were used where the draught was inadequate. The Romans smelted copper at the mines but later ore was carried to smelters with permanent furnaces of stone or brick. By the eighteenth century some were as large as a small cottage.

In Cornwall the first blowing houses were for tin; copper needed higher temperatures and could be smelted only crudely. By law tin had to be smelted in the county but this did not apply to copper. Elizabeth I brought all mines and their products under Crown control and called in German miners from the Harz Mountains to increase productivity. In 1555 a German was given licence to search Cornwall for gold, silver and copper. The Society of Mines Royal, formed in 1568, was concerned with the mining, smelting and refining of copper. The Society had three smelters at Keswick. Its sister company of Mineral and Battery Works made brass and wire at Tintern, Gwent, in the Wye Valley. These were the first attempts at large-scale copper smelting and manufacturing in Britain. Simple blast furnaces remained in use until the reverberatory furnace was introduced a hundred years later.

Higher Bal, Pendeen, about 1900. The mine captain, Captain Nathan White (right), and the purser, Major Dick White (centre), talk to a foundry worker, H. V. B. Corin.

In 1580 Thomas Smith was granted a mining lease in Cornwall, Devon and Cardigan. He engaged a German master miner as manager in Cornwall but his copper mines were unsuccessful. Local fuel supplies were poor so Smith built a smelter at Neath in South Wales. In 1602 Richard Carew, in his *Survey of Cornwall,* showed that copper ore was found in various localities and shipped to Wales for refining. Fluctuating prices affected trade and during the seventeenth century copper mining virtually ceased in Cornwall. Many mines were abandoned during the fighting of the Civil War. However, the Mines Royal Acts of 1689 and 1692 freed copper, lead and tin mines from claims by the Crown; private companies moved in and discovered new metalliferous deposits.

About 1770 it was suggested that it would be just as cheap to import coal to Cornwall as to export copper ore to South Wales. Smelting was tried at St Ives but the venture failed. Ten years later it began again at Penpol, Phillack, close to ports where Welsh coal was unloaded. In 1730 there were six smelting companies in England and Wales — at Swansea, Bristol, Redbrook (Gloucestershire) and Penpol. In 1754 some 'adventurers' proposed buying Cornish copper ore to refine in Cornwall. They built furnaces near Camborne. The main problem was fuel supply. Borlase, a contemporary writer, described how hundreds of mules with panniers full of Welsh coal struggled over difficult ground, carrying coal to the mines and returning laden with copper ore for shipment to South Wales and Bristol.

In 1756 the Cornish Copper Company bought land around Hayle, the best local port near the mines. The river was widened for a dock 100 metres (110 yards) long, which still remains. Fumes from the furnaces determined where buildings were sited. Prevailing south-westerly winds blew sulphurous and arsenic-laden smoke across the area. Heat from the furnaces was intense and explosions occurred as hot metal was poured into wet moulds. Work at the smelter was hard. Young boys tended fires and worked bellows. Unsanitary conditions caused frequent outbreaks of cholera

ABOVE: *Horse-drawn wagons carting ore, South Australia, late nineteenth century.*

BELOW: *Ore was roasted to remove sulphur before smelting. Large lumps were broken by hand. South Australia, late nineteenth century.*

BELOW: *Walleroo, South Australia, 1915. Copper was precipitated electrolytically on to the plates while impurities dropped through as a sludge.*

and fevers. Work at the smelter was little better than work in the mines. Cornish copper smelting came to an end in 1819 when copper from the huge Parys Mountain mine and increasing transport and fuel costs forced the Cornish Copper Company into liquidation.

The copper reverberatory furnace was developed in Swansea, which soon became the world's largest producer. It had a good harbour, high-grade coal was mined nearby and Cornish copper was a short voyage away. Ore was roasted to carry off some of the sulphur, then smelted in a furnace to produce a 'matte'. Air, blown through the molten matte, oxidised iron sulphides, leaving a fluid slag which could be easily run off. More air converted the sulphide to 'blister copper'. This was refined by electrolysis to remove unwanted metals and to recover silver or gold. At the end of the nineteenth century the reverberatory furnaces were 4 metres (13 feet) long: now they may be 40 metres (130 feet) in length. The rise of copper production in the United States destroyed Swansea's monopoly and by the First World War most furnaces had been abandoned.

Since the late nineteenth century there have been great changes in copper production. At that time flotation was first used to recover fine copper ore. Chemicals, added to the finely ground ore dispersed in water, make the chalcopyrite water-repellent. Streams of air bubbles blown upwards cause the copper ore to float to the surface, where it can be scraped off. Waste minerals remain at the bottom of the flotation tank. Froth flotation has revolutionised the recovery of fine copper ore and enabled the working of big, low-grade deposits with disseminated ore. As fine flotation concentrates replaced coarse, hand-picked ore the blast furnace lost its importance and pure copper is now produced in the United States by hydrometallurgy and electrowinning at about one-third of the cost of smelting.

Weighing copper ingots, South Australia, early twentieth century.

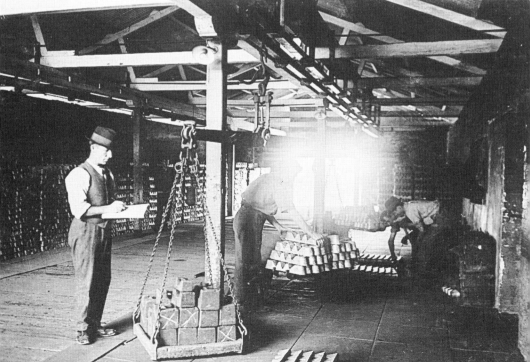

FURTHER READING

Agricola, Georgius. *De Re Metallica*. Translated by H. C. and L. H. Hoover. Dover Publications, 1950. (First published by *The Mining Magazine*, 1912.)

Atkinson, R. L. *Tin and Tin Mining*. Shire Publications, 1985.

Barton, D. B. (editor). *Historic Cornish Mining Scenes Underground*. D. Bradford Barton, 1967.

Bick, D. E. *The Old Metal Mines of Mid-Wales* (parts 1-5). Pound House, 1976-8.

Burt, R. *Devon and Somerset Mines — Metalliferous and Associated Minerals 1845-1913*. University of Exeter and Northern Mine Research Society, 1984.

Carlon, C. J. *The Alderley Edge Copper Mines*. John Sherratt, 1979.

Crowley, T. E. *Beam Engines*. Shire Publications, fourth edition 1986.

Drexel, J. F. *Mining in South Australia — A Pictorial History*. Department of Mines and Energy, South Australia, 1985.

Earl, B. *Cornish Mining*. D. Bradford Barton, 1968.

Edwards, R., and Atkinson, K. *Ore Deposit Geology*. Chapman and Hall, 1986.

Gregory, C. E. *A Concise History of Mining*. Pergamon, 1981.

Hodge, James. *Richard Trevithick*. Shire Publications, 1973.

Holland, Eric G. *Coniston Copper Mines. A Field Guide*. Cicerone Press, 1981.

Joralemon, Ira B. *Copper*. Howell-North Books, 1973.

Madigan, R. J. *Of Minerals and Men*. Australasian IMM, 1981.

Pascoe, W. H. *The History of the Cornish Copper Company*. Dyllansow Truran, 1981.

Prain, Sir Ronald. *Copper — The Anatomy of an Industry*. Mining Journal Books, 1975.

Richardson, J. B. *Metal Mining* (Industrial Archaeology Series 12). Allen Lane, 1974.

Rothenberg, B. *Timna*. Thames and Hudson, 1972.

Skinner, B. J. *Earth Resources* (pages 53-8). Prentice-Hall, 1976.

Smith, B. Webster. *The World's Greatest Copper Mines*. Hoklinson, 1967.

Trounson, J. *Mining in Cornwall* (volumes I and II). Moorland Publishing Company, 1980.

Tylecote, R. F. *A History of Metallurgy*. The Metals Society, London, 1976.

Willies, Lynn. *Lead and Lead Mining*. Shire Publications, 1982.

MINING SOCIETIES

Carn Brea Mining Society: c/o Camborne School of Mines, Pool, Redruth, Cornwall TR15 3SE. Telephone: Camborne (0209) 714866.

Earby Mines Research Group: c/o Earby Mines Museum, The Old Grammar School, School Lane, Earby, Colne, Lancashire.

Northern Mines Research Group: c/o J. H. McNeil, 166 Irlam Road, Flixton, Urmston, Manchester M31 3NB.

Peak District Mines Historical Society: c/o Peak District Mining Museum, The Pavilion, Matlock Bath, Derbyshire.

Plymouth Mineral and Mining Club: 25 Budshead Road, St Budeaux, Plymouth. Telephone: Plymouth (0752) 361375.

Royal Geological Society of Cornwall: West Wing, St John's Hall, Alverton Street, Penzance, Cornwall TR18 2QR.

Trevithick Society: Bill Newby, Gonew Viscoe, Lelant Downs, Hayle, Cornwall TR27 6NH. Telephone: Penzance (0736) 740337.

PLACES TO VISIT

Exploration of old mines is hazardous and the greatest care is required. Never go underground alone or without a guide and the proper equipment.

Local caving and mining clubs such as the Carn Brea Mining Society, the Derbyshire Caving Club and the Shropshire Caving and Mining Club are usually very willing to lead interested parties around old mine workings.

The following museums include items connected with copper or copper mining. Intending visitors are advised to find out the times of opening before making a special journey.

Camborne School of Mines Geological Museum, Trevenson, Pool, Redruth, Cornwall TR15 3SE. Telephone: Camborne (0209) 714886.

Cornish Engines, East Pool Engine Houses, Pool, Redruth, Cornwall. Telephone: Redruth (0209) 216657. National Trust.

Cornwall County Museum, River Street, Truro, Cornwall. Telephone: Truro (0872) 72205.

Earby Mines Museum, The Old Grammar School, School Lane, Earby, Colne, Lancashire.

Morwellham Quay Open Air Museum, Morwellham, Tavistock, Devon PL19 8JL. Telephone: Tavistock (0822) 832766.

Museum of the Royal Geological Society of Cornwall, West Wing, St John's Hall, Alverton Street, Penzance, Cornwall TR18 2QR.

Peak District Mining Museum, The Pavilion, Matlock Bath, Derbyshire. Telephone: Matlock (0629) 3834.

Poldark Mine, Wendron, Helston, Cornwall TR13 0ER. Telephone: Helston (0326) 573173 or 573531.

Sygun Copper Mine, Beddgelert, Caernarfon, Gwynedd LL55 4NE. Telephone: Beddgelert (076 686) 595.

Wheal Martyn China Clay Museum, Carthew, St Austell, Cornwall PL26 8XG. Telephone: St Austell (0726) 850362.

Ball mills for finely grinding copper ore, Cerro Colorado, Spain, 1979.